A birthday candle, a pretty gold ring,
A small puzzle piece, and a crown for a king.

I spy a starfish, the feather of a bird,
Thirty-one cents, and a very SANDY word;

A little baby's footprint, a rattle with bells,
A crab, a fork, and seven seashells.

I spy a snake, a three-letter word,
And flying underneath, a great white bird;

16

Nine gold stars, a blue tube of glitter,
One clay cat, and a six-legged critter.

I spy a stamp, a boy with a plane,
A key on a ring, a song about rain;

Two striped socks, a spaghetti-sauce face,
A girl on a swing, and a snowcapped place.

I spy a wand and ballet slippers,
A bird on a scarf, and fingernail clippers;

A bunny-rabbit mask, a heart-shaped box,
A birthday candle, and a key that locks.

I spy an arrowhead, a little white goose,

A horse's shadow, a snake on the loose;

One egg that's white, another that's blue,
A tiger in the grass, and a small turtle, too.

I spy a lamb, a small silver jack,
A bright yellow pencil, a blue thumbtack;

Two black arrows, a red ladybug,
A little puppy dog, and an Oriental rug.

I spy a clothespin, one silver dime,
A little round face that used to tell time;

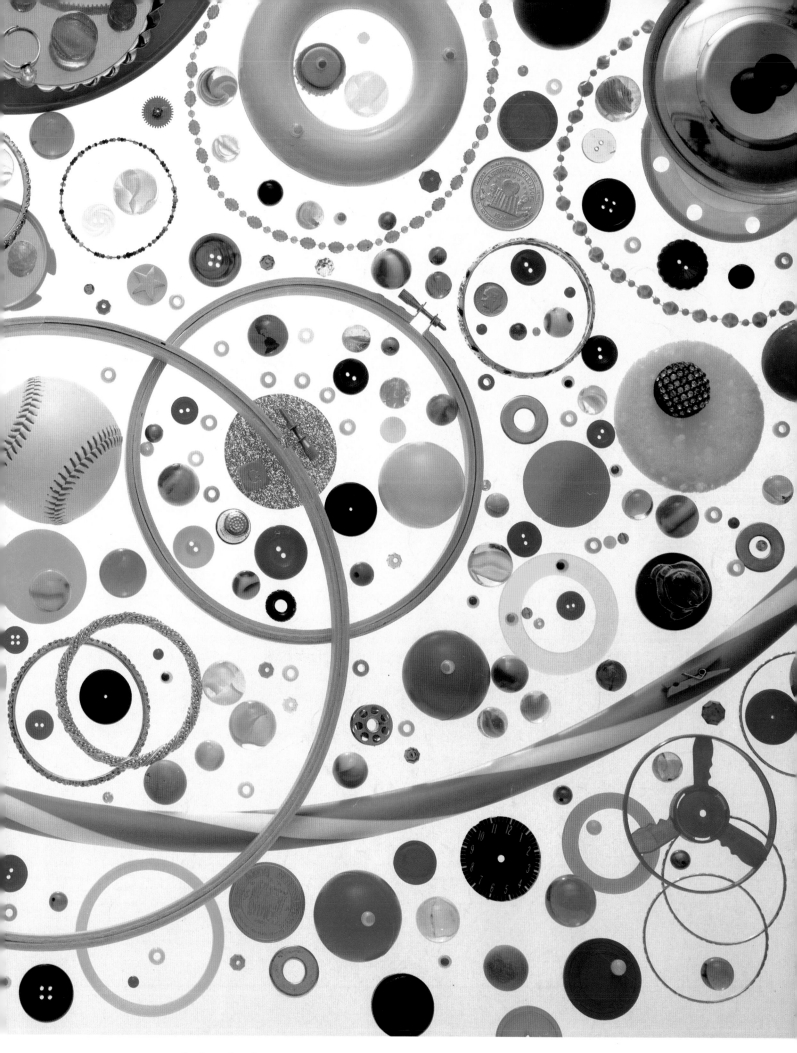

One red ladybug, one gold star;
A new baseball, and a wheel for a car.

I spy a squirt gun, a cowboy hat,
Six airplanes, and a baseball bat;

The point of a pencil, a whistle with a star,
Two yoyos, and a screw near a car.

I spy an eagle, eleven fish with fins,
A yellow paper clip, and ten bowling pins;

A bright red phone, a pink baby shoe,
A spider that's black, and an eight that's blue.

I spy an anchor, a musical note,
A crayon and a snake and a small billy goat;

A pair of sunglasses, a tiny bird cage—
I also spy something from every other page.

EXTRA CREDIT RIDDLES

"Find Me" Riddle

I'm little and green; I live in a bog;

I'm in every picture; I am a _____.

Find the Pictures That Go with These Riddles:

I spy six matches, an electric plug,

A double-decker cone, and a little black bug.

I spy a squirrel, a small blue pail,

A penny in a boat, and one little nail.

I spy three hearts, a bat and a ball,

One king's crown, and five 5's in all.

I spy a jar, a small striped stone,

An old flowerpot, and antlers of bone.

I spy a butterfly, a little pearl ring,

One king's crown, and a toy with a string.

I spy a fish and a small cutting tool,

A craftstick doll, and thread on a spool.

I spy a swan, two silly clowns,

An Indian chief, and two gold crowns.

I spy a blimp, an American flag,

A silver safety pin, and a small price tag.

I spy a sea horse, a lonely flip-flop,

A little fisherman, and a buried bottle top.

I spy a reindeer, a colorful parrot,

A thimble with a plant, and a little orange carrot.

I spy a fish hook nearby a hen,

An elephant, egg, and a ballpoint pen.

I spy a clown and a pretty white glove,

A small white horse, and a couple in love.

I spy a globe, an upside-down heart,

Three sports trophies, and a little red cart.

Write Your Own Picture Riddles

There are many more hidden objects and many more possibilities for riddles in this book. Write some rhyming picture riddles yourself, and try them out with friends.

Jean Marzollo has written many books for children, including *Pretend You're a Cat, Baby Unicorn, The Green Ghost of Appleville, The Best Present Ever,* and *In 1492.*

Ms. Marzollo is also the editor of Scholastic's kindergarten magazine, *Let's Find Out,* which is designed by **Carol Devine Carson.**

Walter Wick is the inventor of many photographic puzzles for *Games* magazine, and is a free-lance photographer for Scholastic's *Let's Find Out* and *Super Science.* His credits include over 300 magazine and book covers including *Newsweek, Fortune,* and *Psychology Today.*

Mr. Wick lives in New York City. This is his first book for Scholastic.